The THINKING Book

by Adelaide Holl
Elementary School Teacher
Worthington, Ohio

pictures by Dagmar Wilson

GOLDEN PRESS • NEW YORK

distributed by

ENCYCLOPÆDIA BRITANNICA

CHICAGO

Name the animals.
Tell the colors of each one.

5

Find a home for each of these animals.

Say the name of the animal.

Say the name of the place it lives.

6

Here are riddles for you to guess.
The pictures will help you.

I am long and thin.
I do not have any feet.
What is my name?

I am heart-shaped.
I am red with blue
and yellow flowers
on me.
What am I?

I am round.
I am orange.
I have a smiling face.
What am I?

8

I am green.
I carry a little round
house on my back.
What is my name?

I am square.
I am red and yellow.
I have a letter of the
alphabet on me.
What am I?

I am shaped like a star.
I live in the sea.
What is my name?

Find a fat clown.
Find a tall clown.
Which clowns have happy faces?
Which clowns have sad faces?
Why is this a funny picture?

11

How do you know that the children
are going to school?
What shows you that it is autumn?

How do you know that it is winter?

How do you know that it is Betty's birthday?
What tells you that she is five years old?

Something in the picture tells you
about the weather outside.
Are you a good detective?

Tom and Sue are going to the swimming pool.
Help them find the right path to take.

14

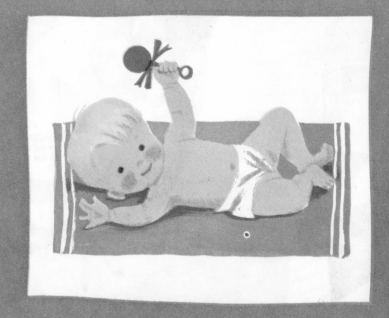

What will I be when I grow up?
Find my picture on the next page.

16

Why do you think the kitten ran up the tree?
How do you suppose he will get down?

Point to all the people.
Name them.
How many people
are in your family?
Say their names.

Find some things you could use
to make a birdhouse.
Find some things you could use
to make cookies.
Find some things you could use
to make a doll dress.

20

Name the things on this page.
Tell how each one is useful.
Look about you.
What other useful things
do you have in your house?

What do you think the boy should do?
Tell about something polite
you have done for someone.

Can you find some children
who are being kind and helpful?
Tell about the picture.

23

Do You Know?

Who lives in a house of glass so round
And never, never makes a sound?

Who lives in a small wire house that swings
And sings and sings and sings and sings?

Who lives in a straw house in a tree
And hides her babies from you and me?

Who lives in a hollow tree in a wood
That he fills with nuts for his winter food?

Who lives in a house with Father and Mother
And maybe a sister and maybe a brother?

—Ethel M. Wegert

Bobby is going for a walk.
What things in the picture show
that Bobby is in the city?

Nancy is helping her mother.
How do you know that Nancy lives in the country?
Can you think of some farm animals
that are not in this picture?

Find a child who is hopping.
Find somebody who is jumping.
What other things are the children doing?
Name some other playground games that are fun.

31

You can name all the animals in the pet parade,
but can you name the children?
Here are some clues to help you.
Jane is the first one in the parade.
Bill is the last one.
Tommy is the tallest boy.
Betty is wearing a blue dress and white socks.

Make up a name for each
of the other children.

Point to each picture and say its name.

Find two things that go on land.

Find two things that go in water.

How many of these can fly in the air?

Tell about some ways *you* have traveled.

34

Look at this row of pictures.

A skunk, a squirrel, and a rabbit are all animals.

A drum is not an animal. Drum is out of place.

Find something in each row of pictures that is out of place.

A Rainy Day

Down the puddly street they go,
Bright umbrellas in a row.
Count the red ones—one, two, three.
How many blue ones do you see?

How many are there altogether
in the rainy, rainy weather?

How many things in the picture
show you that it is a rainy day?

A Windy Day

What shows you that the wind is blowing?

37

PUPPET
THEATER

38

Fun with Boxes

How are the children having fun with boxes?
Tell about the picture.

Find a big box.
With the help of someone in your family,
make something with the box.

Little Raccoon's Dinner Time

It is evening in the woods.
Little Raccoon is awake.
He will come out of his tree hole
and go down to the stream
to catch a fish for dinner.

Little Raccoon will find
other forest animals
at the stream.
Can you name the animals?

Find the twins in each row.

All Kinds of Hats

On Monday, Jimmy's an Engineer.

On Tuesday, he's Fireman Jim.

On Wednesday, a Pirate so bad and bold
That hanging's too good for him!

On Thursday, he launches his rocket ship
And zooms off into space.

On Friday, he may be an Indian Chief
With a savage, painted face,

Or a Big League pitcher on the mound—
Or maybe he's up to bat.

On Saturday, Jimmy is Cowboy Jim
In a ten-gallon cowboy hat,
Waylaid by a band of enemies
And shooting them left and right—

But on Sunday, Jimmy is only James,
And he's *glad* when it's Sunday night.

—*Kathryn Jackson*

Pretend *you* are a Big League ball player.
Show how you would pitch a ball.
Show how you would bat a ball.
Pretend you are other people in the poem.

45

At the Farm

Which hen has many babies?

Which hen has none?

Which basket is full?

Which basket is empty?

Teddy has all the apples.
Point to Teddy.

Sally has more flowers than Jane.
Point to Sally.

47

The Tree House

Father is helping the boys build a tree house.
Father is making the floor. Point to Father.
Don is putting on the roof. Which boy is Don?
Stevie is making a table for the tree house.
Which one is Stevie?
Tell why you think a tree house would be fun.

Holiday Fun

Tell a story about the pictures.

50

Doing Things for Yourself

Tell what each of these children is doing.

52

How many of these things can you do all by yourself?

Listen to the poem. Try to guess the secret.
The pictures will help you guess.

The Secret

We have a secret, just we three,
The robin, and I, and the cherry tree;
The bird told the tree, and the tree told me,
And nobody knows it but just us three.

But of course the robin knows it best,
Because she built the—I shan't tell the rest;
And laid the four little—something in it—
I'm afraid I shall tell it every minute.

But if the tree and the robin don't peep,
I'll try *my* best the secret to keep;
Though I know when the little birds fly about
Then the whole secret will be out.

—*Anonymous*

Things We Wear

The pictures show some different
things to wear.
Some are for girls.
Some are for boys.
Name each thing.
Tell on which part of the body
you would wear it.

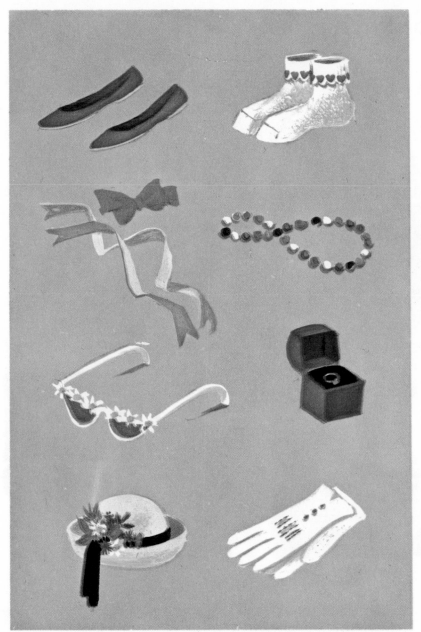
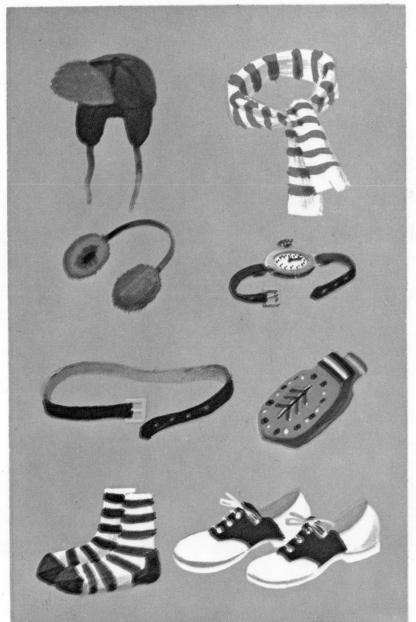

Words That Rhyme

Look at the pictures in each square. Say the words for the pictures.

The words sound alike. The words rhyme.

Help read this poem.
Say the rhyming words.
The pictures will help you.

Who is sitting on the log?
One little spotted _____ .

Count the puppies—one, two.
They are chewing on a _____ .

Three tiny kittens in the house
Are playing with a catnip _____ .

What other rhyming words can you think of?

Smells

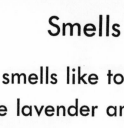

My Daddy smells like tobacco and books,
Mother, like lavender and listerine;
Uncle John carries a whiff of cigars;
Nannie smells starchy and soapy and clean.

Shandy, my dog, has a smell of his own
(When he's been out in the rain he smells most);
But Katie, the cook, is more splendid than all—
She smells exactly like hot buttered toast!

—Christopher Morley

Name some things that you like to smell.

60

The Picnic

Name all the good things to eat.
Which ones taste sweet?
Which ones taste salty?
Which ones are juicy?
What foods do you like to eat?
Tell how they taste.

61

Name these things.
Which would feel smooth?

Name the animals.
Which ones would feel fuzzy?

Name some things that feel sharp when you touch them.
Touch some different things in your house.
Tell how each one feels.